Panda's
Surprise

by Chyng Feng Sun
illustrated by Michael Grejniec

HOUGHTON MIFFLIN COMPANY

BOSTON

ATLANTA   DALLAS   GENEVA, ILLINOIS   PALO ALTO   PRINCETON

It was Panda's birthday

and he wanted to have fun all day.

He went to see Tiger.
"Do you want to have some fun with me?"
Panda asked.

"Not now," said Tiger.
"I'm making something."
"What are you making?" Panda asked.
"Oh, it's a secret," said Tiger.
  She hid something yellow under her paw.

5

So Panda went to see Monkey.
"Do you want to have some fun with me?"
Panda asked.

"Not now," said Monkey.
"I'm making something."
"What are you making?" Panda asked.
"Oh, it's a secret," said Monkey.
He hid something red under his tail.

So Panda went to see Sheep.
"Do you want to have some fun with me?"
Panda asked.

"Not now," said Sheep.
"I'm making something."
"What are you making?" Panda asked.
"Oh, it's a secret," said Sheep.
  She hid something blue behind her horns.

9

"Everybody is busy," said Panda.
"But it is my birthday,
 and I want to have fun all day.
 I will just have to have some fun by myse

And he did.
Panda had lots of fun.

He climbed trees.

He made a swing.

He stood on his head.

He played in a mud puddle.

Panda made a funny hat.
He sang songs all the way home.
Guess who was waiting for him there?

SURPRISE!
It was Tiger, Monkey, and Sheep,
and they all had birthday presents!

"Oh, boy!" cried Panda. "Thanks!
I'm ready to have some more fun now."

And they did.